This Walker book belongs to:

_____

_____

_____

First published 1988 and 2004 in *Out and About*
and *Olly and Me* by Walker Books Ltd
87 Vauxhall Walk, London SE11 5HJ

This edition published 2016

2 4 6 8 10 9 7 5 3 1

This book has been typeset in Plantin Light Educational

Printed in China

British Library Cataloguing in Publication Data:
a catalogue record for this book is available from the British Library

ISBN 978-1-4063-7281-6

www.walker.co.uk

THE NURSERY COLLECTION

SUMMER

Shirley Hughes

WALKER BOOKS
AND SUBSIDIARIES

LONDON • BOSTON • SYDNEY • AUCKLAND

Squirting Rainbows
Bare legs,
Bare toes,
Paddling pool,
Garden hose.
Daisies sprinkled
In the grass,
Dandelions
Bold as brass.
Squirting rainbows,
Sunbeam flashes,
Backyard full
Of shrieks and splashes!

Water

I like water.
The shallow, splashy, paddly kind,
The hold-on-tight-it's-deep kind.

Splosh it out of buckets,
Spray it all around.

I *do* like water.

Car Ride

We're in the car,
Strapped in our seats.
We sit and we sit,
Looking at other cars
And the backs of trucks.
Olly is cross,
Bemily's feeling sick,
As we watch the lampposts
Gliding past – fast!
Like people in a long, long line.
And still we sit.
Olly sucks his thumb
And dozes off.
I've got my book
But I still look
At the huge signs
(which I can't read)
And the places for petrol,
And the lampposts,
Rushing past.
And I wish and I wish we were there.

Then, at last,
We stop!
Olly wakes up
(Still cross)
But we're there!
We're there, in the bright air!
And we're walking on grass.

Seaside

Sand in the sandwiches,
Sand in the tea,
Flat, wet sand running
Down to the sea.
Pools full of seaweed,
Shells and stones,
Damp bathing suits
And ice-cream cones.

Waves pouring in
To a sand-castle moat.
Mend the defences!
Now we're afloat!
Water's for splashing,
Sand is for play,
A day by the sea
Is the best kind of day.

Sand

I like sand.

The run-between-your-fingers kind,

The build-it-into-castles kind.

Mountains of sand meeting the sky,

Flat sand, going on for ever,

I *do* like sand.

The Grass House

The grass house
Is my private place.
Nobody can see me
In the grass house.
Feathery plumes
Meet over my head.
Down here,
In the green, there are:
Seeds
Weeds
Stalks
Pods
And tiny little flowers.

Only the cat
And some busy, hurrying ants
Know where my grass house is.

Splishing and Splashing

Deep in the green shade
Two mums sit, lazily chatting.

But Norah and I are busy,
Turning the tap,
Filling buckets
And the watering can,
Slooshing in it;
Making mud,
Making rivers and dams
And swimming pools for ants.

Olly's busy too,
Sitting in a basin of water,
Bailing out.

Sunshine at Bedtime

Streets full of blossom,
Like pink and white snow,
Beds full of tulips,
Tucked up in a row.

Trees full of "candles"
Alight in the park,
Sunshine at bedtime,
Why isn't it dark?

Yet high in the sky
I saw the moon,
Pale as a ghost
In the afternoon.